Seeing the Light While Living with Cancer

Seeing the Light While Living with Cancer

How Adversity Can Teach Us to Live a Meaningful Life

Elliott A. Schulman, MD
Moss Jackson, PhD

Foreword by Erik Zeger, MD

DEDICATION

This book is dedicated to all those fighting pancreatic cancer
and to all those who are focused on defeating this terrible disease.
You are all fighting the good fight.

TABLE OF CONTENTS

Commentary by Moss Jackson, PhD.

FOREWORD

How will you cope with the life-threatening diagnosis of cancer? If you are reading this, you or someone you know was likely recently diagnosed with cancer. This must be one of the most difficult times of your life. This is the fight of your life.

As an oncologist for nearly 20 years, I have been with many patients and families on this journey. It is not an easy one. Invariably, in the beginning, there are so many emotions; fear, sadness, depression, and even anger.

They can be consuming and paralyzing for some. The diagnosis and treatment can be isolating. However, there is a path forward through this initial darkness, which hopefully, will allow you to see the light.

Learn from Dr. Elliott Schulman's journey. While I have been with Elliott from the beginning of his cancer journey, we have known each other professionally for years as colleagues at Lankenau Medical Center. His resilience and bravery have guided him through many difficult times since his diagnosis of pancreatic cancer.

The first several months were so difficult for him. Sadness was ever present. Fear of a lost future with his wife, Bonnie, and sons. The threat of a career as a physician cut short.

This perspective changed Elliott. As he began writing this book there was a clear and evident transformation. A shift away from the negative emotions towards positivity and hope. Learn from his story.

Always the physician, he wrote this book to help you on your journey. I am sure you will find his insights helpful in your fight with cancer. You are not alone. Build your support team and get to work.

Erik Zeger, MD

WHY I AM WRITING THIS HANDBOOK

It has been more than 12 months since I was diagnosed with pancreatic cancer. Over this time, I have gained several insights. The most important reason for writing this handbook is to share my perspective on how my disease has affected me and its impact on how I view life.

First, I needed to switch my roles from being a physician to being a patient. I knew I couldn't make medical decisions for myself. I lacked the skill set for this area of medicine, and my years of experience had taught me that proper treatment required the judgment of an objective physician, always balancing its risk with its benefit. Besides, expertise in oncology is both an art and a science, the former being something I sorely lacked.

I now faced dark days and needed to adopt a new set of tools to optimize my mood, to learn that, despite it all, there are silver linings that I have now recognized. In addition, I needed to find purpose. I have always enjoyed writing, and this was the perfect opportunity to continue that interest. This book also provided a distraction which I found to be effective in keeping me focused which, in turn, helped to keep my anxieties and depression at bay.

I hope that writing this book will provide information to other patients with cancer and to their families. This handbook contains a paucity of medical information. This is not a medical resource in the traditional sense. This is not a "how-to" publication, but hopefully it will provide some suggestions on coping with your disease.

This disease will change you. It will make you examine your life, your accomplishments, your relationships. My reflections and insights won't apply to everyone, but I hope they will provide you with a new perspective on your disease.

I have a fresh outlook on my struggles, my interactions, and what is important in this stage in my life. I would not have wished for this disease, but I have grown in ways I could never have imagined. Rather than this disease limiting me, it has provided me an appreciation for life events that have helped shape me.

Finally, this book is a way for me to examine my feelings; a vehicle by which I can express my fears and anger and hopes. It has helped me to view these emotions with objectivity and to address them with clarity.

Elliott Schulman, MD

Dealing with This Disease

Introduction to Pancreatic Cancer

The three most common types of cancer in the US are breast, lung, and colorectal. They may present with symptoms that the patient himself may recognize as being suspicious for cancer (a lump in the breast, a chronic cough, or blood in the stool). Other cancers, such as ovarian, melanoma, or pancreatic, may commonly present only once the disease is advanced.

Pancreatic cancer commonly presents with vague and nonspecific symptoms. There are no early screening tests. Oftentimes, they may be discovered while the patient is being evaluated for an unrelated complaint. Such was the case with me.

I did not consider cancer when I went to my urologist because of difficulty urinating. I felt well otherwise. My physician suspected prostatitis but decided to order a full panel of blood work. Some of my liver tests were elevated, which prompted a CT scan of my abdomen.

Upon further evaluation, I was found to have pancreatic cancer. Even in retrospect, I felt generally well and considered my 5-10 lb. weight loss a result of eliminating desserts. Once the diagnosis was made, I was admitted to the hospital. Within 48 hours a biopsy was done, a stent was inserted to drain my liver, and a port was placed.

Looking back on these days is difficult as they are opaque and blurry in my memory. Multiple physicians, family members, friends, and my Rabbi visited. Important decisions were made. My wife slept at the hospital each night, yet I have no memory of this. Whether I was too sedated, too overwhelmed, or simply blocked it out, I have no recollection of these days.

I found this disturbing. When I was with patients, my concentration was focused. I made sure that my patients heard what I said. Now that I was the patient I was jarred by this unexpected, unprecedented lapse in memory. I am detail-oriented and my illness was something in which I would have insisted on having input as to the course. Was this a normal reaction? Was I so overwhelmed that I couldn't process it?

When unexpected illness strikes, make sure a designated family member keeps notes on which doctors visited, what procedures were done, what decisions were made, as well as any future treatments discussed.

Make sure you are comfortable with your treating physician. The doctors' expertise may not be enough. If you see your physician as being gruff, lacking empathy, or removed, the chemistry may not be right. You need to believe your physician is invested in your care and is accessible.

COMMENTARY

Pancreatic cancer is a stealth illness, presenting often times with few or any symptoms prior to the biopsy and diagnosis. The discussion when the bad news is delivered can be a bewildering experience. Often the doctor delivers devastating medical information about your life without being particularly empathetic.

Elliott reports those early day as being a blur. This can translate into information which is poorly understood and inadequately comprehended. The shock of this diagnosis can trigger a shutdown reaction, rendering the patient incapable of making any well-informed decisions about the treatment process.

Elliott emphasizes the value of having a designated family member present each time you meet with the physician. Your spouse or significant other becomes your "thinking brain" and advocate. They should ask follow-up questions and keep notes to review with you later. They are also able to adequately assess your emotional state and whether your cognition is compromised.

Lastly, Elliott comments about having the right doctor, who usually becomes the captain of the team. It is essential that a sense of trust and mutual respect are present in the doctor-patient relationship. Your life depends on it!

Delivering – and Receiving – the Bad News

I don't remember being scared or anxious when I received my diagnosis. I had delivered bad news to my patients, but now I was the patient. When I spoke to my patients about a test result of concern, I would always try to be precise and gentle, and offer all the options for treatment.

When I was given the diagnosis of cancer, I felt numb. It wasn't the way my doctor delivered the news. It was my acknowledgment about the severity of the disease. I remember considering how devastating this disease was, and instead of being scared, my thoughts turned to those of survival.

Pancreatic cancer is difficult to cure, and its prognosis is poor. For this reason, most healthcare workers fear the diagnosis. Its reputation is well known. The doctors told me I was not a surgical candidate at that time.

Aside from my professional knowledge of pancreatic cancer, I had a personal connection with it. My medical school roommate had died of the disease about 12 years earlier. I remembered his physical and emotional decline. I remembered how his personality could fill a room. It seemed like his charisma would have been powerful enough to ward off this disease.

I remember visiting for the first time after the diagnosis was made. He shared a similar emotion with me. "It's not fair." I thought my special friend was being tested. I wondered if I were in the same situation, would I have his courage, tenacity and determination? I had overcome many struggles in my life, and this would be one more. But how would I measure up?

With my own diagnosis, I pondered how long I could maintain a productive lifestyle. My son had set a wedding date. Would I make it? Would I ever spend time at the Delaware beach again? I was 73 and had chosen not to retire. There was a lot more I wanted to experience.

All these questions swirled around at once. It seemed I couldn't focus on any of them. I usually can prioritize my issues, but not now. When I took stock of my life, I was fortunate. I had a great family and kids, and my friends were devoted and supportive.

And, I had the privilege of becoming a physician. I loved medicine and being a physician. I had always wanted to become a doctor. Besides the desire to become a railroad engineer from ages 6 to 8, my dream was to go into medicine. I remember exactly when I decided.

I was with my mother, who was getting a routine physical. I saw how the physician interacted with her (and me) and I marveled at his ability to understand the workings of the body and its organs. He focused on getting to know his patients as a person and finding how he could help them. And I liked science, enjoyed establishing a rapport with others, and understood that medicine is a helping profession. My mind was made up.

Despite being a practicing neurologist for over 40 years I knew with my diagnosis that my professional life would change. But I also knew that remaining a practicing physician was a priority. Surely with my treatments I'd have to cut back on my office schedule and I worried how sick would I be after chemotherapy and radiation.

My physician explained that my treatment would help to shrink the tumor, and hopefully, would give me the option of a surgical removal of my tumor. It was all different now. My plan to continue to practice was uncertain. Would I be bed-bound, lose my sense of humor, or fail the test?

Some weeks later, I remember feeling hopeless. I cried a lot. I blamed myself for the tumor. What did I do wrong? Why was I being punished? Was God punishing me? Had I not accomplished enough in my life? And if I were to have cancer, why this one? As a physician, I knew there was no logic in placing blame upon myself, but still... why was I afflicted with this disease?

I had turned this disease into one that was my fault. Rather than it being random, it was my doing. This viewpoint didn't help me to think more clearly nor did it allow me to address the issues that I needed to face.

I worried about my family and how this would affect them. I had always promised to be there for my boys, and that they could always count on me. I remember holding my wife's hand. She reminded me we were going to take one day at a time, and today, I thankfully feel well. She is my rock.

Once you have your diagnosis, you need to decide with whom you would like to share the information. Choosing whom to tell was difficult. Which relatives, friends, or even certain patients with whom I'd developed a special rapport, should I tell them? Could they maintain my confidentiality? How would they respond?

I decided to only tell my closest colleagues, some office staff, and a few select relatives and friends. Every time I told the story I cried. I became upset and entered a dark place. Some responded in a gruff fashion. One physician said, "You'll beat it," and then walked away. I was hurt by his response. I felt I was being dismissed, making a big deal out of nothing, when I had hoped for some empathy or comforting words.

Others wanted to know if I made up a "bucket list". I knew the implications of that question. Some wanted to know details of the prognosis and my "chances". Although I consider myself a diplomatic person, I was getting tired of responses that were anything but comforting.

I began telling my friends that these comments were insensitive. I asked them to consider how the remarks would be interpreted by them if the tables were turned. I think they were shocked with my candor, but I needed to send the message that the remarks were hurtful.

I wish I would have asked them for what I needed. And now I realized I needed to put myself first. My needs were the priority. A simple "How are you doing?" Or "can I do anything for you?" would have been enough.

After too many upsetting interactions, I decided to ask my wife to deliver the bad news on my behalf. It was too painful for me to repeat the story again and again. Friends don't know what to say. Oftentimes, their responses can be inappropriate and lacking in empathy.

You can see how complicated these interactions can be. That's why giving friends feedback on their responses can lead to awkward moments. When you are telling people about your disease, the response may be inadvertently insensitive. Be prepared.

Not all my tears were related to being frightened. At other times my tears reflected feeling special; that I mattered to others. I cried when I found that a friend from years ago had heard I was ill and wanted to express concern, love and support.

One friend dedicated an art presentation to me. Some of my friends from grade school called unexpectedly to wish me well. I had never expected to be so emotional. Whether they were good or bad, positive or negative, I experienced more feelings than I knew I ever had.

Get the Facts About Your Disease: You Are Not a Statistic

After the diagnosis is rendered, you undoubtedly will want to learn more about your disease. After speaking with your physician, you can supplement this information with reliable details from the internet.

Patient organizations devoted to your disease will provide credible information. Stick with conventional western medicine, at least as a base. Always let your treating physician know that you plan to get second opinions. There should be no secrets between you and your physician. If he or she objects to another opinion, your physician may not be the best match for you.

I always tell my patients that my job is to get them better. When patients have challenging conditions, I would suggest a second opinion. I would also insist on giving them the name of the physician who I thought was an expert in their field. I also emphasize that they have no obligation to return to me if they find the physician to whom I referred them a better fit.

Patient statistics may be quoted. For some diseases, they may be discouraging. Remember, you are not a statistic. You are an individual and you may do better than the statistics predict. And if you choose not to educate yourself because the information may be overwhelming, that is your choice.

However, you may be presented with options as to what is the next step in your treatment. Make sure you have a good understanding of the choices in terms of success rates, side effects, and whether certain options will preclude other options going forward. Be sure you know if you are entering a trial, and if so, if that will involve a placebo (inactive arm). Regardless, never be afraid to ask questions. I find it's best to come in with a list of the topics you want to cover.

For me, there was another uniquely complex aspect to my treatment: I had always been on the "doctor side" of the doctor-patient relationship. Now I had become the patient. Even though I was a physician, I knew very little about pancreatic cancer. They told me I was not a surgical candidate. I was fortunate because my attending physicians understood that this needed an explanation.

This clarification was provided with patience and in an empathetic fashion. I realized that this is what a patient wants and needs. When I interact with my patients, I will intersperse some humor. It serves to break the ice and makes our interaction more relaxed. Being a patient was, perhaps unexpectedly, making me an even better physician.

The one thing I always mentioned to my physician was my mood. I was often depressed or anxious. I often ask my patients about their mood, but I could not comprehend its true importance until I was the patient. I made a mental note to be more diligent about how my patients' illnesses were affecting their mood and the best way to address it.

COMMENTARY

As you move from the shock phase to the decision-making phase, you become an information gatherer about your condition. Your doctor is your treatment captain, so begin with him. Ask questions about your treatment options. Ask for another consultation. Resist the urge to be become passive. Speak up and ask questions.

Elliott cautions you not to see yourself as a statistic. You are not a statistic, which is simply an analysis of data. You are unique and you are different from others in the pool, making you more than a statistic. Statistics are derived from many treatment studies. They are suggestive, not predictive. Ask your doctor to talk to you about your unique condition, in contrast to what the statistics suggest.

Elliott mentions that he found himself not on the "doctor side" but on the "patient side" of the doctor-patient relationship. This can be quite confusing, yet enlightening, for someone like Elliott who usually has occupied the doctor position. He recognized he was not very knowledgeable or comfortable in this area of medicine. This gave him a better sense of the difficulties other patients experience when they are trying to understand their medical situation.

Am I Being Tested?

This segment does not refer to medical testing. No bloodwork or imaging is involved.

This chapter refers to being "tested", as in, being put into a situation which causes undue stress and excessive demands; a test of someone's fortitude.

I remember seeing a television star who was being interviewed by Barbara Walters. He was fighting a rare cancer. She asked him about his reaction to receiving the diagnosis. There were no tears, but only a look of determination. He said he had always wanted to be tested, and this was his chance.

Being tested means different things to different people. For me it meant coming through the struggle as a winner. Curiously, the thought appealed to me. After all, I had been tested before, and I always was up to the task. Was this just another opportunity to show my tenacity? Did I still have it?

I guess I secretly pondered this question, wondering if I wasn't tested regularly, would I lose my grit and determination? Prior to my diagnosis, I attended fewer meetings, hadn't written any time-consuming research papers, and although still working, it was now part-time.

I started thinking about my father. Thankfully, he was very healthy until his late 80s. At that time, he developed a generalized infection and became less and less responsive. Toward the end, as he was doing poorly, one of his friends from assisted living stopped me to say, "Your Dad told me something I think you should know. He said that if he were to die at this point in his life, he was ready".

He related that my father had accomplished a lot in his life and he was at peace, which was something I needed to think about.

Was I going to surrender to my disease? Although my father was content with the life he lived and what he had accomplished, that wasn't me. I still had much to live for, including my family and friends. And although I wasn't as active in my practice as I had been, I still loved medicine and my patients.

You Were Dealt These Cards, Now Play Them

These words were spoken to me by a good friend, a surgeon, whose father was my aforementioned medical school roommate who had died from pancreatic cancer. His message about playing the cards you were dealt really struck a chord. Although as a physician I knew that my cancer randomly selected me, it was hard to shake the blame I had initially placed upon myself.

What had I done wrong? Is God punishing me because I offended somebody or treated them poorly? I finally accepted that my disease was not a punishment, but part of life's ups and downs. This resolve made me look at it differently. I needed to fight it, almost like I was waging a war. It was time to get out the big guns. Gather the troops.

And just like a card game, be strategic. Think about it as a thing; an adversary in a game; an enemy on the battlefield. To beat it, I was ready for battle, and determined to use all the tools I had at my disposal. My friends provided their support as my army. My wife was appointed the Battalion Commander. I would take the steps and play the hand and wage the war, but I would do none of this alone.

COMMENTARY

Elliott may not have planned to be a warrior, but he became one. I know Elliott to be a caring, generous and an accommodating person, but his "unwelcome visitor" required a very different perspective. Like all people who contract a chronic illness such as cancer, there is a call to arms. There is no more time to be a victim to your disease.

Now is the time to become a survivor and a fighter. Better yet, become a Life Navigator, who brings a sense of grit, determination and realism to the challenge you are facing.

Elliott is up for this battle. He is developing a plan and enrolling a powerful team to help him win. These actions, along with resolute faith, are called realistic optimism: be brutally realistic and maintain a positive view toward your future.

A New Wrinkle: COVID-19

When I was first diagnosed, COVID-19 was not a factor in shaping my daily activities. I remember distracting myself by going to the supermarket with my wife, treating myself to the richest and most delicious ice cream. I loved browsing all the new flavors and picking up other special treats as I walked down the grocery aisle. Then came COVID-19.

I haven't been inside any store in several months. I'm frightened of picking up the virus, especially with my immune-compromised state. Occasionally, we'll take a ride, stop for a soda or a smoothie at a convenience store, and come home. My biggest treat is walking my dogs, oftentimes running into a neighbor along the way.

There was one issue where COVID-19 did come into play, and in a big way. My son and his fiancée got engaged in the summer of 2019 and had planned their wedding for early September 2020. As the date approached, we realized a big wedding wasn't in the cards. This was one of the things that I worried about. Would I be healthy enough to attend?

It wasn't my decision, but I strongly favored a small ceremony, with only immediate family and a few close friends. It was all about the sacred ceremony. The big party could wait another year, when hopefully COVID-19 would not be a factor. I was a bit anxious about our guests not wearing masks or maintaining appropriate social distancing. Thankfully, everyone was COVID-19 appropriate. Regardless, nothing could prevent me from attending my son's wedding.

We all celebrated this special wedding, with 21 guests, heartfelt vows, and lovely toasts. It was perfect! Despite all of the potential distractions, I was fortunate enough to be a part of the wedding and share in the joy. It was a hope that was thankfully realized.

COMMENTARY

The limitations of COVID-19 impose an additional level of stress. No longer are you able to socialize with large groups of friends, attend family gatherings or even engage in mundane activities like shopping at the supermarket. Accept your limitations and be willing to set boundaries to your interactions.

Do not expect others to appreciate your concerns about staying safe. This is not a social decision, but rather a medical one. Some may object or be critical of your concerns, but it is up to you to protect your welfare.

Challenges Ahead

Do Not Let the Disease Define You

Though cancer would undoubtedly impact my life, I was determined not to let the disease define me. I would still be who I was – who I am – but with an additional dimension. Almost a fifth limb or another appendage. Not something I would have wished for, but there, nonetheless. And with all my troops gathered and all my grit mustered, I was determined to beat this adversary.

Because I was very selective about whom I told about my disease, most of my friends and colleagues saw me no differently than prior to my diagnosis. It was me who saw myself differently. Was it defining me? I needed a different label besides cancer. Was it a disability? Maybe I should see it as another challenge in my life path. This made it seem like this was something I could overcome, and not so final.

When I was faced with challenges it was not enough to just overcome them. I wanted to attack them with so much energy that I could decimate them. Almost as though they never existed. Just a name-change, and a new way of dealing with my disease was born. It took me a while to see my disease as a disability and even longer to attack it with the ferocity that I had used in other life challenges.

Until my cancer battle, the biggest challenge that I had faced in my life was getting into medical school. I had worked very hard in college. My university was very competitive in the undergraduate years. There were lots of pre-med students, all taking the required science and math courses. All our grades were marked on a curve, and with many intelligent students competing, it wasn't uncommon to receive a B. Good, but not good enough to get you into medical school.

My downfall was organic chemistry. It just never clicked with me. In this two-semester course I got two Cs in the class and two Ds in lab. These grades dropped my average to below the cutoff for medical school admission.

Despite applying to over 30 schools, I received not one acceptance. Without any advice or consultation, I enrolled in a Master's course in counseling. I told the chair of the department that my eye was on medical school. She encouraged me and was grateful for my candor.

I worked hard, dug in, and hoped for an acceptance the following year. Hard work was my "go to". I was accepted to medical school the following year. Determination and grit were the ingredients to the magic formula then and they still apply to this day. Now it was time to apply it to my 5th appendage, the cancer.

A good friend called me one afternoon. He told me that beating this cancer wasn't that big of a challenge. He said that I had made it through basic training as part of my National Guard obligation. If I could do that, beating cancer was doable.

Basic training was emotionally and physically intimidating, but I knew that determination would see me through. I remember my days in basic training. Long runs, push-ups, and qualifying with a rifle. These were not activities I enjoyed. But I took it all with a simple approach, "One day at a time."

I never looked at the next day's activities (which were often overwhelming), until I readied for bed the night before. I compartmentalized my concerns. I was able to utilize this approach in dealing with my cancer. One day at a time.

I really enjoyed writing medical articles and chapters. Some years ago, I found I just didn't have time to write. All the writing was done at night after my office hours. As I needed a purpose, I have taken to writing this "handbook," hoping it will help patients struggling with cancer. This was my first step in fighting this disease.

COMMENTARY

Elliott is creating a powerful distinction that allows him to take action. He now has an "unwelcome visitor" called cancer. How will he engage with it? Will he become a victim to it and hold it as a disability? How is he to acknowledge its presence, come to terms with it and stay in control?

Elliott reframes the visitor as a "challenge" in his path. This challenge opens possible action moving forward. He remembers other challenges in his life such as getting into medical school and completing basic training. He regains a sense of grit and determination and begins to channel these powerful healing resources to fight his disease. He discovers the challenge of writing a book to help other patients who struggle with cancer.

He is now a man with a purpose.

Change Is Inevitable, So Embrace It

When I was first diagnosed, I monitored my health daily. Did I feel better or worse? Why did my abdomen feel funny? There were days when I couldn't stop crying, with no clear cause. Some days I just felt like being alone.

Each day was different, with some days better than others. Some days, I wish I felt as strong as I had the day before. Before long, with some advice from my therapist, I realized that thankfully my "off" days would not be there forever, and in a few days, I was again feeling strong, both emotionally and physically. I was thankful for these good days. And while not hoping for bad days, I realized that if the cycle recurred, with some luck and positive thinking, good days were on the horizon.

Before I knew it, I realized, that with my disease, like life, change was a constant. And there were good times as well as challenging times. This perspective helped me accept change. And maybe when the down days occurred, I could worry less, continue working on maintaining a positive attitude, and hopefully, look for better days ahead.

COMMENTARY

Change is inevitable. Someone once wrote, "The only person who wishes for a change is a baby with a wet diaper." When you have cancer, inherent in the disease are changes your body may experience.

Elliott is learning to flow with the changes in his body and his life. As he writes, "Some days are good and others are not."

The key is to appreciate your good days when your energy and mood are strong and positive. When you slip into a low energy state and experience a depressed mood, do your best to keep things in perspective. The cycle will soon shift and you will again feel more energy and less hopefulness.

Allow yourself some self-compassion and love, and appreciation. You are not failing or doing anything wrong. You are just feeling sad, scared, or upset. Have your feelings and get on with the day.

Roadblocks and Advocacy

Health is mercurial. Your symptoms may change in intensity and progression. Your lab results may yield disappointments and pleasant surprises, punctuated by both good and bad days. It can feel like a roller coaster. Sometimes these fluctuations are related to extrinsic factors, including mistakes in scheduling, assumptions about the treatment you were to receive, and your insurance company denying a test or medicine.

Try to remember that these roadblocks will occur and are not uncommon. Regardless, you need to be the forklift that moves them aside and so it is important to discuss patient advocacy.

Being your own advocate can feel simultaneously empowering and arduous. When you have cancer, so many things feel out of control, so maintaining control, in ways large or small, will help your mood. However, there are times when you may be physically or emotionally exhausted and that is why fortifying your team of advocates is salient. Some of these roadblocks may be health-related, and some are simply bureaucratic.

For example, if you can't get a specific drug because it's not on the formulary, or if a test is not approved by your insurance, don't hesitate to advocate for the best care possible, either directly, or through a trusted member of your team. Although your doctor may need to appeal the decision, you can start by calling the insurance company yourself or enlisting the aid of your employer's HR office. It is important to recruit those who can help you resolve these issues.

Having a medical advocate is more complicated. It is usually someone who has a working knowledge of medicine, but ideally, it is someone who also understands the emotional impact of your disease. In theory, it could be your physician or the nurse caring for you.

Only those who have a medical background may realize when a wound wasn't cultured, the urine has turned bloody, or the pulse is hovering at a dangerously high level. If you don't have a medically trained advocate, don't be afraid to ask questions to the medical staff.

Gathering information is a form of advocacy. I suggest writing things down. This is important when you are told an order for pain meds was to be written and hours later the analgesic has not been dispensed, the CT scan ordered the day prior was not done, or that a consultant never wrote a note. In my experience, questions to the nurses and doctors signal an interest by the patient's family.

The medical team should be open to questions, and they should be answered to your satisfaction. Be firm, but gracious. Kindness, respect, and patience go a long way. If there is no one in your life who can do this, then hire someone to do it (known as a Care Manager). Patients with an ongoing illness must have an advocate. It is often too taxing to shoulder everything on your own.

Family members, especially those who are detail-oriented and strong, can also prove to be incredibly effective advocates. If you are impaired, be sure a family member has an ongoing dialogue with your physicians regarding your diagnosis, treatment plan, and expectations. This comes into play when a patient lacks the ability to make decisions regarding their care or choosing a treatment option. I suggest you plan ahead and make things as clear as possible.

An advance directive has information about your preferences for care in the event you become too sick to make your own decisions. It is a legal document. It guides your loved ones and doctors to make the appropriate decisions based on your wishes. An advance directive has two parts:

The first part, the healthcare power of attorney, names the person or people you want to make decisions on your behalf.

The second part is the living will, which contains your preferences for the medical care you receive. Your family members will undoubtedly be emotional during this time, so making things as clear as possible is actually a gift to them and, ultimately, to yourself.

I have always understood the importance of advocacy as a physician, but I gained vast perspective from my own illness. This was emphasized as the result of a recent procedure. After the placement of a biliary stent, I was discharged from the short procedure unit. This was the third time I had either had a stent placed or exchanged, and the previous procedures were uneventful.

Later that night, I awoke with shaking chills and a fever. Fortunately, my wife bundled me up and took me to the Emergency Room. She was not allowed in because of COVID-19. Before I knew it, I found myself in the ICU, being asked if I had a living will and if I had a power of attorney. It was only then that I realized how ill I was.

I was hospitalized for a week, and a few weeks later, had my gallbladder removed. During each of the hospitalizations I was allowed no visitors because of COVID-19. During my first hospitalization, I was unclear as to my diagnosis as a result of my sedating medicines and the severity of my illness. I was scared and crying.

First, let me say this was a very uncommon complication of a stent placement. And it did fall under the category of "roadblock". However, because of the severity of my illness and its abrupt onset, I was not prepared for it. I am certain the fact that I was not allowed visitors further complicated the situation. It did reinforce my guidelines for tackling unforeseen obstacles.

Sometimes your frustrations with these procedural barriers are magnified by concerns about your disease. Focus on the problems at hand and move on. A victory can boost your spirits and embolden you for other obstacles that lie ahead. Never let these roadblocks distract from your primary goal of addressing your disease.

COMMENTARY

Elliott writes about the ups and downs of the treatment process. Get used to it. They are part and parcel of treatment. Mistakes happen, disappointments occur, doctors forget, and your family will not always rise to the challenge. They are not doing anything wrong on purpose. They are just human beings trying to do their best.

At times, you will create your own roadblocks. Your frustration and sadness may get the best of you, and it may cause you to become angry. This negative thinking will bully you into thinking all is lost. Your therapist, spouse, and medical advocates are there to support you through the treatment process. Share your concerns so they understand what you need.

You must clearly communicate your desires.

Modify Emotional Triggers

Since my diagnosis, my emotions have been generally expressed by crying. Crying didn't always mean I was upset. Sometimes I cried because I was touched by another's concern, their kind words, or their generosity. Their words truly brought me comfort, reflected caring, and were genuine. All these accolades were more than I ever anticipated, and, in response, I cried tears of gratitude.

But, much more often, I cried because of anxiety, fear, or depression. Despite all my work trying to balance my emotions, I often could not control my crying. Maybe if I could identify my triggers, I could better control my negative emotions.

My illness scared me. After all, I didn't know my future and I had little control. I certainly was entitled to cry, and I had received permission from my therapist to cry if I wanted. But were there additional reasons I cried?

In examining this question, I realized there were several. I worried about my wife and sons. If it came to pass, could they manage without me? I didn't want to leave my family. I had more to do in life. I wanted to spend more time with my family, continue seeing patients and travel (post-COVID).

But maybe I was also scared of dying. I'd met patients in the hospital who told me they weren't scared of death. My father expressed that when he passed, he would be at peace. Some patients expressed a wish to die. "I'm too frail" or "everything hurts" or "I'm tired of fighting" were common refrains. I wasn't there yet, and I wanted to fight the fight.

Was some of my crying "learned", perhaps? I remember that when I was in medical school, my mother needed a hysterectomy. I spoke to her OB-Gyn. There were some abnormal cells on a Pap smear, but the prognosis was excellent. A few days after surgery, my mother was walking the halls. I was sorry my Mom needed surgery, but happy that she was likely to do well.

There was one thing I remember, though. It was her crying.

I knew she was thinking the worst. She came by this naturally. My mother had been brought up during the depression and had experienced lots of stress and uncertainty. She often spoke of this. The ongoing stress of the financial depression led her to be anxious and oftentimes sparked negative emotions, sometimes expressed in crying.

I remember being mystified as a medical student, seeing very ill patients being admitted to the hospital. I could not believe they weren't outwardly crying or palpably anxious and had simply decided to take one day at a time, facing their diseases head-on. I saw other patients who faced cancer, never shedding a tear. They were calm, determined, and focused.

I once asked my therapist why I cried more than others and I was told I am more sensitive than others. I accepted that as an explanation, but maybe some of my crying was also learned; a combination of nature and nurture. If I could recognize this crying as (at least partially) a learned behavior, maybe I'd be able to find better balance on my emotional tightrope.

I want to emphasize that crying is not a behavior to be ashamed of. It reflects my anger, frustration, or emotional pain. For me, it was a way I dealt with this disease. It can be cathartic, as after crying, I often feel better. Managing it is the key. With acceptance comes control.

If you can reframe crying, allowing it to convey a deliberate processing of emotions, you are empowering yourself. If you allow yourself to believe the lie that crying only conveys weakness you will be depriving yourself an incredibly effective coping skill.

COMMENTARY

Life is hard enough without cancer. There are multiple triggers that can precipitate a stress reaction. It could be an unexpected bill, a phone call not returned, a broken promise, a failed sales call, or getting sick.

A chronic illness can increase our stress reaction, triggering more intense sadness and despair, frustration, irritability and loss of focus. We can forget how blessed our life is, what to be grateful for, and the support of loved ones. We fall into the role of a victim.

Elliott writes about how his illness frightened him. It is easy to worry, not only about yourself, but also your loved ones and their future. The illness can evoke memories of past hurts, failures, and disappointments. Whatever stress reactions you had before, they may be exacerbated.

Your sadness becomes despair, anger becomes rage, and worry becomes terror. It is important to recognize triggers and learn calming and self-regenerative practices. Find ways to express upset, such as having a good cry, exercising, yelling in the shower, or talking to your family and friends. No shame is required; just let go.

Cancer is a Disease That Affects the Family

My family knew I was experiencing stress related to my tumor. It was compounded by the COVID-19 pandemic, and its impact on our lives. I worried about my wife and my sons.

How were they dealing with it? Did my crying add to their stress? And when I saw valued friends, I usually cried, which I imagined was not the welcome they had hoped for.

In some families, one family member may be the designated caregiver when other members are ill. Sometimes this is the role they wish to assume. Other times, they are the caregiver by default because no one else is willing to assume it.

They are responsible for determining who will pay the bills, make sure the meds are taken, prepare the meals, or give them a ride to physician appointments. Excuses include living too far away, being too busy at work, their own family issues, or illness. This may breed resentment in the caregiver.

This is a very complicated and sensitive subject for the family. A family meeting can be extremely beneficial, so that all issues can be discussed openly. And in some situations, the emphasis must be on giving the caregiver time to recharge.

Such a respite may allow the caregiver time for the gym, a nap, or time to visit with close friends. It can also include something as simple as bringing in dinner. If possible, family members and friends should all assume some role in delivering care.

COMMENTARY

This observation is right on target. I remember several years ago, I became quite ill and needed lengthy rehabilitation services and considerable time at home to recover. My acupuncturist told me I would do fine because of my positive attitude and all the medical support I would receive.

She was concerned about the impact of my illness on my chief caretaker, my wife. Her caution proved prophetic. After several months, I was back on my feet and back to my busy schedule. My wife, unfortunately, became depressed and it took more than a year for her to recover.

If the illness is chronic and debilitating, there may be a time when difficult decisions need to be made regarding treatments, financial arrangements, home care, etc. This is the time for the entire family to talk about the challenge they now face and how each member will share in the care taking.

This scenario may precipitate family unity or division. A medical crisis often brings out the best and worst in a family. With some careful planning, families can most certainly experience the former.

Positivity

Silver Linings and the "Gratitude Countdown"

With all of the negativity, fear, sadness, and pain around this terrible disease, I had an insight more surprising than any other: gratitude. Prior to my battle, I could never have imagined this unexpected, yet welcomed consequence; that out of this trying time I would find something positive, even a silver lining. With the help of my wife and therapist, I began to see life differently. I was thankful for my good days, and for all the positives in life I had been blessed with.

Among them was marrying my wife of almost 40 years. Although most of our friends regale on her baking, she is much more. She is a woman whose strength and resilience has served her well. Although we came from different backgrounds, we have forged a relationship based on trust, mutual respect and communication.

I was so fortunate to have married a wonderful woman. She always encouraged, calmed me, helped me see the light. And my wonderful sons and new special daughter-in-law were all kind, caring, and genuine people. I had much to be thankful for.

I was fortunate enough to realize my life's dream of becoming a physician. As a neurologist, and one interested in headache, I knew that untoward life events, stressors, a dysfunctional family and lack of a nurturing childhood, could all promote pain and depression in my patients.

Very few patients had a perfect upbringing. A difficult childhood can color your attitude on life, leading to poor choices and dark places. Since I wasn't in a happy place, I decided to look for some tools to help me address my mood. I quickly realized that in everyone's life some rain must fall. This was my shower.

I invested in a wonderful App called "Calm." It instructs you on meditation, deals with negative emotions, and provides tools for achieving peace. One segment is hosted by Tamara Levitt and is called "Gratitude Countdown." This refers to listing five things we can be thankful for each day.

They can include our supporters, our family, a beautiful flower, or a great night's sleep. It makes me appreciate those things I often took for granted. It keeps me in the moment. My mind doesn't wander into those dark places while I'm compiling my list. Most importantly, it allows me to count my blessings.

Sometimes getting out of those dark places is very difficult. Early on in life, I realized I was born with an extra dose of the "worry gene". In some ways, it served me well. I was never a procrastinator, always prepared for tests, and focused on my grades. It helped me reach my goals. Now, however, it was contributing to my dour mood. I needed to use all my tools to get me out of this funk. And focus on the fact that time would bring a better day.

One daily chore that keeps me on track is my "to do" list. It lists all the things I want to want to accomplish. I've always had a chore list. I always feel a sense of accomplishment when I finish the last item on my list. More than anything else, it keeps me focused and productive.

COMMENTARY

At the entrance to many Asian Temples, two awesome animal statues stand at attention. One represents danger and the other hope. To enter the sanctuary, one must bring forth birth, courage, and love.

Cancer is a crisis for both patient and family. The word "crisis", like the two statues at the Temple's entrance, representing danger/anxiety and opportunity/hope.

Elliott writes about finding a deep level of gratitude for his blessings. He is embracing the opportunity and "hope" part of his crisis. Not just the dreaded and fearful part. It is a powerful daily practice to reflect on what you are grateful for and value in life. Your illness can bring a silver lining in the form of appreciating your experiences and relationships.

Be in the Moment and Appreciate the Day

Each day we are bombarded by negative thoughts. They include worries about the future, a lot of "what-ifs", and sometimes, exploring dark places. I find it very difficult to chase away the bad thoughts, but we only have today, and now. We don't know what tomorrow will bring. We need to lean on our faith and hope to make it a good day. It takes effort to be in the moment. Meditation and prayer help, and distraction through purposeful activity keep us in the present. We can also gain strength and peace by speaking to supportive relatives and friends.

My wife is very good at keeping me in the moment. When I just can't get a grip, my wife grabs my hand, looks me in the eye and says, "You're here today. Thankfully, you feel well; let's focus on that."

It works.

I have also become an expert in distraction. One activity that has served as a distraction is spending time at the beach, where I am content watching and listening to the waves. I love to walk in town, eat ice cream, or spend time reading. I watch my movies on Netflix, read on my kindle, or listen to my favorite bands with my headphones on. These all distract me from places I wish to avoid.

COMMENTARY

Sartre, the French writer wrote, "You do not have to wait until you die to be in hell, just spending each day in your regrets and resentments." Dwelling on the past provokes regret and rumination about what might happen in the future and promotes anxiety.

Focus on one thing at a time, give yourself a pat on the back when you complete a task, enjoy easy conversation with a friend, play a game, or watch a TV series you enjoy. Notice when you get pulled into "hell" and resist the urge to dwell on negative thinking. You have a life to live so make sure you appreciate each moment.

A Good Attitude Is the Best Medicine

Our capacity to live with and effectively manage chronic illness can be influenced by the way we view ourselves. Physical and mental health go hand in hand, each one influencing the other. It is a cycle of sorts in which our physical illness causes emotional stress which, in turn, compromises our immune system's ability to heal.

If you can improve your mental health, you are giving yourself a chance to positively impact your physical health. Sleep, nutrition, and a positive attitude are all key in fortifying our bodies and minds.

We are beginning to understand the biochemical basis for this symbiotic relationship. The sympathetic nervous system controls the fight-or-flight response to stress. While the stress response can be adaptive, it also impairs the immune system, if prolonged. The protective effect of certain immune cells (T cells) is diminished and their function is impaired.

Being resilient is an important quality to possess when fighting cancer. It is something that can be developed and strengthened, particularly with appropriate support from our social networks and health care professionals. We need to optimize all facets of our being when confronted with ill health.

COMMENTARY

What you think and feel impacts your emotional and physical health. Negative thoughts such as ruminating, fretting, and worrying impact your body adversely, causing damage to your cardiovascular, digestive and immune systems. To better deal with your cancer, you need to modulate your nervous system by using constructive thinking and adopting a positive attitude.

You do not have to be a prisoner or victim to your troublesome and destructive thoughts. You can learn to improve your health. Bruce Lipton, the biologist, writes about the power of your thoughts in his book entitled, *The Power of Belief: Unleashing the Power of Consciousness, Matter and Miracles.* To paraphrase, "change your thinking, change your beliefs; change your beliefs, change your brain; change your brain, change your destiny." This is referred to as epigenetics.

Epigenetic changes are DNA changes that do not affect the DNA sequence but impact gene activity. This concept that you could affect changes in your brain by thinking positively was popularized by the book *The Power of Positive Thinking* by Norman Vincent Peale. Be positive and you will become positive.

Useful Tools

Meditation and Prayer

The mediation I practice is based on focused breathing. Ideally, you can redirect your (sometimes toxic) wandering thoughts. Instead, you can focus on the act of breathing and combine it with focused relaxation. No matter how bad my day is going, I have designated time for myself for this activity. I am getting better and better at chasing out those dark thoughts.

Meditation allows you to be distracted from your concerns and promotes a relaxed state. There is serenity in "simply being". You practice letting your emotions rise and pass. You adopt a state of openness and acknowledge your emotions, without being judgmental. This "me time" allows me to clear my mind and experience a calmness, which helps me reset.

Sometimes taking a step back helps. I found that when I was caught in that tornado of worry, the winds got faster, and the worry more intense. It was difficult to free myself from all the chaos. Self-talk, distraction, and mindfulness often did the trick.

Praying is a different experience for each of us. It depends on your religion, how you were brought up, and what you believe constitutes God or some other higher power. For me, it allows me to connect to my God, other congregants, and my Judaism. Even though I can't hear God talking, I believe he hears and sees me.

When I was in my early teens, I regularly attended religious services. We typically went through the prayers in a very standardized fashion. As I grew older, I decided I wanted to devote some time to prayer that best suited my mood and events of the week. Now I could pray for the healing of specific people, the end of COVID-19, the well-being of our country. This manner of prayer was more akin to meditation, for I was alone with my thoughts.

I again embraced prayer. But now with COVID-19, we never prayed together in the sanctuary. We used Zoom video conferencing, where my wife and I could magically appear on a small screen with others, and participate in services. It was easy, and there was a new dimension to connecting. I found this fulfilling and it allowed me to connect with my religion.

Besides praying for healing, I ask for the strength and grit to conquer this disease, and guidance to show me the way. I often speak to the clergy, who bring me inspiration and peace. I pray for my family whom I love, my friends who support me, and ask God to be with me. One of the most inspirational pieces of advice came from my Rabbi. I was going through a time of stress and turmoil.

My Rabbi told me not to be afraid, as God was "holding my hand." Now I find that God is holding one hand, and my wife the other. You could never find better partners.

COMMENTARY

The mind can be a dangerous place to visit for prolonged periods. Humans seem to have worrisome minds that can be quite negative. Most people ruminate about their past regrets, and dread what might happen in the future. This makes sense from an evolutionary perspective. Our ancestors survived predators because of their vigilance and constant preparation for altercations.

Even though these threats do not exist now, our brains have not changed that much in the past 50,000 years. We retain the survival mindset that life is dangerous and remain on guard.

Focused breathing, mindfulness practices, and religious faith help calm our anxious minds and worries. Worrying about your worries just makes you more worried. It takes practice, but you can calm and center yourself with these exercises. Deep breathing calms your nervous system and meditation helps you to focus on something other than your worries. God, along with his wife, Bonnie, help Elliott walk through the darker days with a sense of faith, love, and strength.

Faith and Hope

In the biblical sense, faith is a complete trust or confidence in a higher power. Faith is the belief that there is more that exists, and not limited to only that which we can prove. And although there is no test that proves the presence of God, or a higher power, we have faith in his being, his power and warmth, and his ability to watch over us.

Our faith makes us believe that God guides our experiences. While we may not understand the logic of his actions, we maintain our faith. Hope is a confident expectation that naturally stems from faith. Hope is the belief that we can make things better. With illness, when there is no hope, there is an empty vessel.

To quote Desmond Tutu, "Hope is being able to see that there is light despite all of the darkness." In his book co-authored with the Dalai Lama, entitled *The Book of Joy: Lasting Happiness in a Changing World*, Tutu goes on to explain, "To choose hope is to step firmly forward into the howling wind, baring one's chest to the elements, knowing that, in time, the storm will pass."

Hope must be embraced by the individual, for it gives us meaning.

Find a Therapist You Trust

Despite all the support you may receive from friends and family, I strongly recommend you secure a therapist. Cancer can be a frightening disease. You may feel out of control. Well-meaning family members and friends may suggest specific doctors, hospitals, or even treatments. Your future is unknown, despite reassurance.

You are entitled to your feelings of anxiety, but these feelings should be acknowledged and discussed. It is the job of your treating physician to recommend seeing a therapist if they believe it is indicated. This serves to acknowledge their concern and opens the topic for further discussion. For my patients, I tell them I believe there is a mood issue, and suggest it be addressed. When the diagnosis comes from a physician, it serves to legitimize it and adds to its credibility. The diagnosis goes on the problem list and can be discussed on subsequent office visits.

Friends may soothe you, but a therapist assists with insights and advice, and sees things differently than a friend. Therapists can supply words and perspectives that make a stressful time more tolerable. Find a counselor with whom you feel comfortable speaking. Friends and family lack the professional training that will be of most benefit. They may even create more anxiety and depression.

A non-therapist may tire of your calls. With a psychiatrist or psychologist, your confidentiality is protected, it allows for some access between sessions, and most of all, creates a therapeutic relationship. If you are seeing a psychologist, they may recommend a psychiatrist for a medication consult. Psychologists are unable to prescribe medications but recognize that medications prescribed by a psychiatrist may improve your mood. A therapist can also be skilled in suggesting a psychiatrist who may be a good match for you.

Patients I see who are depressed or anxious may say they don't like to see a therapist. Perhaps you haven't found a therapist who is a good match for you. Finding the right therapist may require an initial interview, a recommendation, and being open to exploring new professional relationships.

I have been very fortunate to have a long-term therapist who was available almost immediately after my diagnosis. My wife always attends my sessions and we share our worries in a calm, neutral setting.

Be prepared to invest the time necessary to make your relationship a successful one. Besides facing cancer, your mood may be a result of additional stressors beyond your current disease, like, in my case, COVID-19. A lack of coping skills can prevent you from moving forward.

For therapy to be successful, you need to be a compliant, responsible participant in the process. You need to be open with your counselor, willing to explore your feelings. Medication alone won't adequately address your mood.

A major reason that therapy is so difficult for some is that the process explores painful memories and experiences. In order to more forward, these issues must be aired. Oftentimes, these discussions raise untoward emotions. Hard work is required, but worth it, promoting growth. Your perspective will change, and your coping skills will be sharpened.

COMMENTARY

Therapy is a powerful resource to help you stay focused, capable, and calm. Given that the mind is negatively biased, and emotions will get triggered throughout your illness, a trusted therapist helps to counterbalance the negativity. Inside the therapeutic relationship, anything can be discussed.

Here is where you can deeply express your deepest worries, regrets, anger, and confusion. It is also where you can learn to be resilient, to cope, problem solve, and self-regulate. You can learn to overcome emotional flooding you may experience, and to use tools to control your upset. Friends and family are helpful, but they do not have the ability to see you through the ups and downs. They may get worn down by your emotions. Spare them the responsibility as much as possible.

Put Yourself First. Trust Your Gut

My whole life I had been a giver. I enjoyed this role. I hoped it made me a better husband, father and physician. I enjoyed taking the time to be a patient advocate. I was a "go with the flow" kind of guy. I didn't require a whole lot to make me happy.

My cancer shifted this part of me. When friends wished to speak or visit when I wasn't up for these things, I became anxious. Sometimes I just wanted to be by myself. Yet I did not want to offend anyone. A good friend gave me excellent advice: your priority should be doing what makes you feel most comfortable. Put yourself first.

One very old friend went six months after my diagnosis before calling me. He was aware of the illness the day after the biopsy was done. He passed me on the street, barely acknowledging me. My wife ran into them and politely asked why they hadn't called. Their response was that they were afraid to call.

Afraid of what? Afraid to talk to me because it might make them feel bad, or make me feel awkward? Were they unsure of what to say? I thought this was a selfish response. I was glad my wife asked why we hadn't heard from them since my diagnosis. She certainly sent a message and was putting me first.

Putting myself first also meant that I could express emotion around others. Initially, I was reluctant to show emotion to others. I felt I was a wimp or weak. But my emotions were genuine and appropriate. Besides, after crying, I always felt better.

Doing what worked for me was something that took some getting used to, but I adapted. I liked having some control, and I spent much less time deliberating over decisions that drained my energy. I realized that putting myself first did not mean I was being selfish; rather, I was being fair to myself.

COMMENTARY

Givers are great to be around. They tend to be caring and generous with their time, attention and personal resources. Elliott has only so much energy at his disposal. Cancer is energy-depleting. He must devote much of his energy to deal with his condition.

While he will probably retain an ongoing caring and giving disposition, he sees the necessity to take charge of himself. For some of you who are givers, this can be a difficult challenge. Take Elliott's advice. Put yourself first. Your life depends on it and you might like the change once you get used to it.

Be Productive

Unless your disease or its treatment render you too ill to function, you should be productive. Being productive means different things to different people. The dictionary defines productive as "being effective at externally rewarding tasks."

Some activities that come to mind include working at a food bank, volunteering at a hospital, delivering meals, or being a companion to someone who is too ill to leave their apartment. Unfortunately, the restrictions associated with the COVID virus impose limitations on our ability to be as productive as we would like. I wanted to be productive doing something I enjoyed and that may benefit the community as well as myself. A tough order to fill.

I am fortunate because this handbook allowed me to pursue my love of writing. I circulated my first draft and my reviewer encouraged me to include personal examples of my concepts. This prompted me to explore my experiences and gain further insights. These helped me emotionally and gave me the opportunity to share them with my readers.

Certainly, writing a short story, a poem, or journaling your experiences could be ways to ventilate. Painting a scene that inspires you, taking up photography, reading all those books that you bought along the way, or starting a blog are productive activities. These are just a few suggestions, but they all serve the function of optimizing each day and can help to distract you from a dark place.

COMMENTARY

Accomplishment feels good to most people. Doing something at work or on a volunteer basis allows us to feel we are contributing. An illness like cancer can cause us to feel less whole and complete.

If you take on a challenge like Elliott did in writing this handbook, you maintain a connection to the world. Elliott took on the challenge of sharing his experience with all of us. It is as if he stood at the entrance to the Asian Temple, looked at the two statues representing anxiety and opportunity, and he took on both.

He faced and continues to face his fears and sadness, along with participating in life with his family, friends, and patients with love and courage.

Compartmentalize

Having pancreatic cancer is a battle you fight every day, sometimes every hour.

Now pretend you're on trial (perhaps an impeachment), trying to save your marriage, mending fences with your daughter. And you happen to be President of the United States, running a country, dealing with daily crises, making decisions that affect millions of citizens. How do you handle all these bouncing balls? You do just what Bill Clinton did: compartmentalize!

And so it can be with us. Focus on one room while keeping the other doors shut. We can do this with our illness.

When I am treating patients, nothing else matters except what is in that room. When I'm with my family, I devote all my attention to them. My cancer is far from my mind, buried deep, and not in a place where I need to address it at that moment.

"Compartmentalization is what allows us to focus," said Sharyn Wolf, a psychotherapist. I used this when faced with COVID-19. I was upset, but I could live with it. Sure, l missed seeing my friends, going out to dinner, and attending concerts, but I couldn't let the virus get in the way of my current situation. I had my disease to focus on. I also used the time when I was writing this book and seeing patients to distract myself.

Compartmentalization is a bit like meditation and deep prayer combined with distraction at its highest level. It allows us to be free of anxiety and worry, while being productive. You need to be disciplined. It is a defense mechanism, or a coping strategy. It requires isolating and focusing on difficult issues separately. Put the challenges in your pocket and banish them from your mind until you are prepared to deal with them in a constructive fashion.

COMMENTARY

Many of my clients get flooded with anxiety, overreact, take things personally, feel misunderstood and victimized. This is usually the result of emotional flooding and getting bounced around by competing and usually negative thoughts. For Elliott or anyone with an illness they might be thinking:

"What does this pain mean? Is the cancer spreading?"

"The doctor told me he would get back to me with the results. He has not called. It must be bad news."

"I can't believe my kids haven't called me. They know I am in bad shape and they should be checking up on me."

"I'm crying again. What's wrong with me?"

Sometimes I suggest my clients keep a journal and write down all their worrisome, negative and miserable thoughts and questions. Writing slows down the speed of the galloping anxiety caused by jumping from one thought to another.

The idea is to get the thoughts out of your head and onto paper. Writing slows your thinking down and you will not feel so flooded and overwhelmed. Be a "thought tracker" and pursue every random thought and write them down.

After you catch your breath, you can look them over and see if there is an underlying theme such as loss of control, not having enough information, feeling disconnected from others, stressing over your uncertain future, etc.

Elliott is learning to compartmentalize, a cognitive skill which allows him to focus on one thing at a time. Focus on the task at hand, the phone calls you are making, cooking dinner or chatting with a friend. If you feel the urge to worry, find a convenient time to spend fifteen minutes just focusing on your worrisome thoughts. Write them down and ask yourself if your worries are really true or imaginary.

Also ask yourself what it is you want that the worry is covering over. Is it information? Is it talking to the doctor or doctor's assistant? Is it wanting connection with a loved one or friend? The point is to focus on one thing at a time...

Imagine being on a tennis court and I serve a ball to you. The objective is to keep your eye on the ball and return the serve. If I hit you another ball too quickly, you will probably get distracted and miss the ball. Imagine if I then hit three, four or five balls. You would be overwhelmed and unable to return a ball.

Getting flooded with multiple thoughts, especially negative ones, is like playing tennis and trying to hit too many balls. The brain wants you to keep things simple and do one thing at a time, the art of compartmentalization and focus.

Elliott has a life to live. He is learning how to focus and be disciplined by "putting his problems in his pocket" and waiting until he finds a time to deal with them. He is learning to hit one ball at a time.

Embrace Those Meaningful in Your Life

During stressful times we seek comfort, and comfort comes with the familiar. This applies to food, old worn clothes, but also to close family and friends. My illness has brought me closer to my family and friends. I always cherished my relationship with my immediate family.

Now my family and I always exchange "I love you," before ending a telephone conversation. They have seen me cry and understand why. They understand how precious they are to me. I am fortunate to have this connection with my wife, my sons and my daughter-in-law.

You also need to be selective with whom you surround yourself with. Don't forget, now you have the choice as to who gets into your inner circle. Those who want to know the details of your disease, takers who ignore your wishes, and those who make insensitive remarks are not allowed beyond the red velvet rope. You get to decide who falls into the meaningful category. Those who express caring and support, while understanding your limits, are welcome.

I've felt empowered by telling individuals that their remarks were hurtful and insensitive, sending a strong message. Some learned to be sensitive, others not so much. I especially like it when friends come to visit and my disease or its treatment are not mentioned. A brief, "How are you?" is enough.

I remember when my medical school roommate was initially diagnosed with pancreatic cancer. I called a well-respected oncologist in my hospital and asked him what to say to my old roommate. His response was to tell him that he was in my thoughts. His advice seemed woefully inadequate. Who ever thought that years later I'd be hoping to get that same support when a friend called to check on me?

COMMENTARY

For those of you who have family and friends to support you, you are fortunate. Their words and wishes are woefully inadequate at times. It is their presence and support that bring us comfort.

Recognize that as much they want to see you heal, their wishes are poorly communicated. Being present, holding their hand, and praying for them, may bring them the peace they seek.

Reconnect

Several years ago, I was sitting in my office, preparing to see a new patient. I briefly scanned her chart and noticed she was a nurse working at a local hospital. I had worked at this hospital previously, having left three years prior for my present employer, a large health care system. We began to talk and I realized she now worked in the same unit as my previous nurse practitioner.

The NP and I had worked closely for three years before she decided to move to a different unit. We understood each other, and I had confidence in her clinical skills. I saw her as a special friend, much more than co-worker. She had a prized place in my heart, exchanging holiday cards and telephone calls. It was about a year since I had last spoken to her.

"And how is Angela doing?" I asked. There was a pause, and my new patient told me she had passed.

I was filled with emotion. I experienced immediate sadness, and a deep sense regret. I never had a chance to say goodbye. There were so many things I would have said to close the circle. I called her husband, expressing condolences, letting him know I was so sorry. Apparently, she passed quickly after discovering her disease. I felt a little better after talking to her husband, but there were thoughts of what I would have shared with her. And now it was too late.

That experience taught me so much. How many other Angelas are out there with whom I had lost touch? People who occupied a warm place in my heart, but I had grown too busy to reach out to. People who were important to me, but whom we had both failed to keep up with. Those who I had been so comfortable with, that even after years of not speaking, I could easily pick up our relationship again, sharing my deepest thoughts, laughing and reminiscing like we had just spoken the day before.

Now I was determined to renew my friendship with those special friends. This was a regret I didn't want to experience again. I began to reconnect. And, beautifully, each old friend became a new friend, again. The rekindling has been effortless and satisfying.

Once I was diagnosed with my tumor, I kept a running mental list of the people I wanted to share my diagnosis with. I knew they would want to know. And I knew they would support me, giving me the encouragement that would help me beat my cancer. Reconnecting was something that I enjoyed and left me feeling satisfied.

COMMENTARY

Connecting with others and forming emotional bonds are two major factors in living a long and healthy life. Humans are social beings who need the contact, conversation and support that others provide. In today's busy, demanding, and stressful world it is easy to lose track of those whose relationships we once cherished.

An illness or crisis such as cancer can remind us of the finite time we have and the opportunity to reconnect with past friends and colleagues.

Accept Support; Encourage It

Now that you are calling the shots, you have some license to reach out to others and ask for support. I remember thinking that I wished I could speak to an old friend. I believed that telling them would illicit a response that would be comforting and meaningful to me, and so I finally reached out and shared my diagnosis. My friend was glad that I had informed him, responding with compassion. We are now in contact on a regular basis.

Sometimes I would go several months between texts from an individual wishing me well. This prompted me to call those individuals telling them that hearing from them made my day.

Sure enough, a week later, I received a text wishing me well or that they were thinking about me. I always responded with a telephone call, another text, or a simple thank you. I was taking care of myself, and hopefully it brought fulfillment to my supporter, knowing that they had brought me some comfort.

Despite my suggestions on how to best seek support, I've learned that not all are able to lend comfort. They are scared they may ask the wrong question, will be embarrassed or feel awkward. As much as I'd like to have their support, I've given up hoping. They just don't have the right equipment to supply the words I need to hear.

No sense in getting angry and wasting energy trying to persuade somebody to do something they can't. There are more important issues you are addressing. Give them a pass, accept that they are trying the best they can, and move on.

COMMENTARY

Humans are social animals who thrive in receiving and giving care, support and encouragement. Life is stressful and unpredictable enough without having a chronic health condition. A person can get triggered by a medical report or blood test.

In an instant, you can become flooded by negative thoughts and depressed feelings. A kind and caring message or conversation can go a long way to lift one's spirits and ease the feeling of isolation and anxiety.

Hold Hands and Paws

One way of providing support is to hold hands with someone who can bring you peace and comfort. Holding hands conveys more than public affection. When a son holds his mother's hand, it can convey support. It also symbolizes, "I'm here," and I promise to connect with you. This simple act serves to enhance the spoken word. It sends the message that I am your constant and I will support you.

I would be remiss if I didn't mention how much love and support my dogs bring me. Both are from a rescue shelter. One sleeps in our bed, the other on the floor in our bedroom. I enjoy their enthusiasm when they see me walk through the door. And I get to walk them, which gets me outside and gives me a bit of exercise.

Any family that has a member with a chronic illness, unless there is a contraindication, should have a dog or cat. They bring happiness, a calm and are wonderful companions. My dogs, Lilly and Jax, provide comfort and love.

COMMENTARY

So simple, yet so true! Physical contact can be reassuring and comforting. Words do not have to be even spoken. The warmth of human touch, hand or paw of a dog or cat creates a connection where you feel calmed, cared for and loved. Indeed, love is healing.

Fellow Patients Can Inspire You

As we seek comfort and support from friends and family, we may find it in other less obvious places. I have found inspiration from other patients I have met while in chemotherapy, or friends who were also facing cancer. I will classify them into three groups. They are the "ultimate givers", the "resolute faithful", the "compassionate ones". From each of these groups, I have been inspired, and encouraged to push myself a bit further in a quest for peace.

The idea of chemotherapy frightened me. I remember worrying about the possible side effects I might encounter. Initially, my wife sat with me, but when the risk of COVID-19 became apparent, she was no longer able to accompany me during chemo. I usually busied myself with reading, telephone calls, just relaxing, or talking with others who were undergoing chemo.

I became friendly with some of the patients whose chemo schedule overlapped with mine. One of the patients I met was Mr. R. Mr. R. was a big imposing man who was suffering from metastatic cancer. He walked slowly, his voice was hoarse, but he was rarely without a smile. It turned out we had lived near each other before he moved to a more friendly one-floor condo. Our wives knew each other, and we struck up a conversation.

I asked him how he stayed so peaceful, facing the burden of his disease. "I come here, get my chemo, and hope for the best. What more can I do?" He had made peace with his disease. The next week I saw him assume the role of an "ultimate giver". A lady sitting a few seats away from him was new to our group. In a non-imposing manner, he asked her if she was new to chemo. She nodded her head yes. He asked if she had any questions, or if she'd like for him to tell her how the process usually went. She nodded no. He asked if she would like water or a snack. Again, she silently declined the offer.

She finished a short time before him, and as she left, his smile turned to a frown. He voiced his disappointment, wishing he could have made her first chemo treatment less intimidating. He was an inspiration, one who could reach out and give, despite of his disease.

An old friend who had been battling cancer for several years was deteriorating. Her chemo was less effective. I called her to offer some support. There I was crying, scared, and she reversed the role. She began to comfort me. I asked her how she was able to maintain her peaceful demeanor. But I didn't need to wait for the answer. A very religious woman, she had her faith. I saw what faith and hope can provide to those facing uncertain times.

I watch the chemo nurses perform their job. Always kind, patient, empathetic, and understanding. Once, I was having a particularly difficult day while getting chemo. Chemo is not painful and I usually tolerate it without too much difficulty. However, when I walk into chemo it makes me remember why I'm there. It's real. I do have this disease. As good as I am about always trying to avoid dark places, chemo brings me right back.

On one particular day, I started crying. It just snuck up on me. My nurse came over as I apologized for crying. Being compassionate, she told me an apology was not necessary. I was meant to feel safe in that space and crying sometimes came when you were in an accepting space, filled with healthcare workers who were experts at acknowledging your feelings, and knowing just the right response.

These are just three examples of those who have inspired me. There are many others. When you are fortunate to meet those who inspire, learn from them and remember the moment.

COMMENTARY

Elliott spoke of a connection he formed with a fellow patient. Each knows what the other is going through and can walk in his shoes with empathy and grace. Elliott, his fellow patients, and the medical staff form an invisible alliance which allows each to learn invaluable lessons which focus on empathy and support.

When You Are Being Sucked In

There are certain times when you feel like your day just won't go the way you'd like it to. You've hit a roadblock, you aren't feeling your best, you woke up on the wrong side of the bed. You are just in a bad place. And sometimes your mind ends up taking you to darker places, even when things are not as bad as they seem.

You've done meditation and prayer, called a few friends for support, and tried to divert your attention. You are just not making any headway. You feel stuck, feeling sad, crying and there seems like there is no way out.

My wife has turned to me and suggested I rely on the lessons I outlined in the book. After all, I wrote this book to help others. My intent was to be an advocate for others. And here, I couldn't even help myself.

I learned there are some days that that are just difficult, sad, challenging days. Your swirling mind won't let you get grounded enough to utilize the tools I've supplied. Accept it. As I've said earlier, you and your disease fluctuate. Today is one of those days. Turn on a favorite comedy or TV show and remember tomorrow will be better.

COMMENTARY

Sometimes people have a bad day. Sometimes they have a terrible day. Elliott is having one of those terrible days, days where the darkness, anxiety and hopelessness overwhelm any sense of joy, and self-control. On days like this, the bleak voice of illness screams so loud that a person cannot hear the other internal voices of self-compassion and hope. What friends and loved ones have to say are not helpful and you feel utterly alone, wondering if the mental anguish will ever stop.

Today, Elliott has been emotionally hijacked. The limbic system in his brain is flooding his thinking brain with massive traffic of anxiety and poor self-control.

Imagine driving into a city on a ten-lane highway system filled with speeding cars hurling along at eighty miles an hour. Then picture one small dirt road coming from the opposite side with one lane to drive on. The emotional hijacking and limbic flooding are the superhighway and the small, one lane coming back is Elliott's thinking brain trying to calm things down. No way! The ten-lane highway wins the day.

The result is the inability to calm yourself down, redirect your thinking and to keep perspective. The terrible day feels like a terrible life, one that will never end. No wonder Elliott is having a "bad day." Perhaps you can relate to this terrible experience where worry, sadness and despair seem to be wherever you are.

I know I have experienced such days. There was a time where Elliott would suffer from a string of "bad days." Friends could not help, nor his family. Attempts at meditation, breathing exercises to calm down the noise in his mind were of little avail. His little dirt road that helped to regulate emotional upsets could not be found, just the noise of a highway out of control.

Now, with the help of a trusted therapist, the love and support of his wife, friends and family, and writing this book, Elliott's one lane has grown bigger and he is able to better navigate the noise in his mind. While he still has pain and worry, he can acknowledge what he is thinking and feeling, talk about it and keep perspective. He can refocus and watch a comedy or enjoy time with his wife and friends. He can see that his bad day does not mean it is terrible and it will pass. He is learning how to use the tools he has developed and to not despair. He is learning to disrupt the negative thinking and catch his breath.

Like Scarlett O'Hara in "Gone With The Wind" who, after surviving the devastation of the Civil War, death of her child and being left by her husband, would defiantly say to herself, "Well, tomorrow is another day," Elliott can face the day and remind himself that his tomorrow will be a better day, too.

As I Continue My Journey

My reason for writing this book was to look at cancer from a different viewpoint. Yes, it is a disease and certainly one you would not wish for, but this challenge you now face can change your perspective on life. It allows you to see others in a fresh light, appreciate all your blessings, and help you take things one day at a time.

I never, however, anticipated that this book would bring me the clarity and peace I have gained. As I continue my journey, I look forward to further growth as I direct my energies to defeating this disease.

One page, one tear, one affirmation, and one day at a time.

ABOUT THE AUTHORS

DR. ELLIOTT SCHULMAN was born in Buffalo, N.Y. After his graduation from medical school, he trained at Georgetown University Hospital, finishing his residency in Neurology.

He moved to the suburbs of Philadelphia, where he continues to practice Neurology. His special interests include Refractory Headache and the effect of abuse on migraine headache prevalence. He has written several scientific papers and has lectured extensively. He is married and has two sons, and a new daughter-in-law, as well as two rescue dogs, Lilly and Jax.

He was diagnosed with pancreatic cancer in December, 2019.

DR. MOSS JACKSON is a clinical psychologist who is Founder and Director of the Center for Psychological Services in Ardmore, PA. Along with a focus on treating anxiety, trauma and PTSD, Dr. Jackson has developed strategies to enhance well-being through energy healing and belief management.

He is also a Success Coach and has helped athletes, coaches, leaders and adolescents to reduce performance anxiety and increase performance excellence. He was an initial presenter at the 2005 RAADfest Conference where he presented on, "The Psychology of Immortality."

He is the author of four other books and is currently working on his fifth, entitled, "Anxiety Sucks, You Don't Have to Suffer." He was diagnosed with pancreatic cancer in 2010. He is now alive and well, practicing his craft and enjoying time at his beach house with his wife, Judy, their children and three grandchildren.

ACKNOWLEDGMENTS

This book would not have been possible without the loving support of my wife of 38 years, Bonnie. She has the knack to calm me, allow me to focus, and take on day at a time. Bonnie is truly my rock and my Brigadier General.

I must thank my two sons, David and Andrew, and my special daughter-in-law, Adrienne, all of whom expressed their caring, support and empathy. And listened, patiently to my bad jokes, and still accepted my crying.

And to all those in "Elliott's Army" who supported me, encouraged me, and reminded me of basic training. I need to single out my sister, who gives me daily telephone calls and a shoulder to lean on. Her words brought me to a place where I could appreciate all my blessings.

And to Moss Jackson, my co-author, whose comments gave my experiences a sense of legitimacy. And to his wife, Judy, my therapist, whose patience, availability, and wise words help me gain perspective on life and this disease.

And a special thank you to my doctors, especially Dr. Erik Zeger and Dr. Mark O'Hara, my oncologists. And to the urology nurse practitioner, Pauline, who ordered an additional panel of bloodwork, just to be thorough. Her diligence led to the discovery of my pancreatic cancer. And the infusion nurses whose empathy is endless.

I would be remiss if I didn't mention my medical school roommate and great friend, Howie, who suffered from pancreatic cancer. His courage and persistence were an inspiration.

And thank you to Rebecca Fox Starr, a special person, whose editing and suggestions helped make the book what it is

And a special appreciation to my son David, who invested his energy, time and imagination into creating a website and helping with the layout and editing of this book.

Finally, a special thank you to Rose Disanto, who helped with all the details of this book as well as crafting a cover, and her support and patience.

RESOURCES

Pancreatic Cancer Action Network

1-877-272-6226

www.pancan.org

American Cancer Society

1-800-227-2345
www.cancer.org

National Cancer Institute

1-800-422-6237
www.cancer.gov

Clinical Trials for Patients and Caregivers

1-800-422-6237

www.cancer.gov/about-cancer/treatment/clinical-trials

Cancer Support Community

1-888-793-9355

cancersupportcommunity.org

American Psychosocial Oncology Society

1-866-276-7443

apos-society.org

WORKS CITED

1. Abrams, Douglas Carlton, Dali Lama, and Desmond Tutu. *The Book of Joy: Lasting Happiness in a Changing World.* Avery, 2016.

2. Lipton, Bruce. *The Power of Belief: Unleashing the Power of Consciousness, Matter and Miracles.* Hay House, 2016.

3. Peale, Norman Vincent. *The Power of Positive Thinking.* Prentice Hall, 1952.

4. Alexandra Jacobs, *"Clinton's a Compartmentalizer-Are You?",* Observer, 01/11/99

Made in the USA
Middletown, DE
03 October 2021

49531015R00056